THUNDERBIRDS
...TO THE RESCUE

**Edited and compiled by
Alan Fennell**

RAVETTE BOOKS

© 1991 ITC Entertainment Group Ltd.
Licensed by Copyright Promotions Ltd.

Edited and compiled by Alan Fennell.

Artwork by Frank Bellamy, Steve Kyte and Graham Bleathman.

All rights reserved.

First published by Ravette Books Limited 1992.
Reprinted 1992

Printed and bound for Ravette Books Limited
3 Glenside Estate, Star Road,
Partridge Green, Horsham,
West Sussex RH13 8RA
An Egmont Company
by Proost International Bookproduction, Belgium

ISBN: 1 85304 406 7

Contents

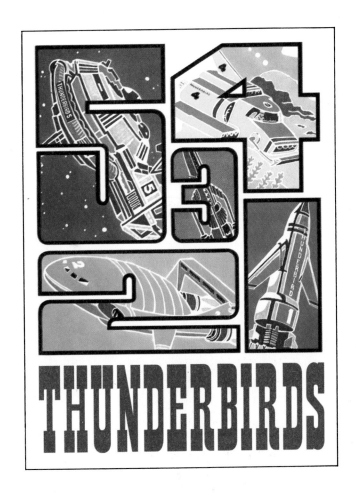

FROM ALL OVER THE CITY, MEN, WOMEN, AND CHILDREN FLOCK TO SAFETY...

SCOTT MUST HAVE ORGANISED THE FIRE-FIGHTING TEAMS, BRAINS. THE FLAMES ARE BEING HELD!

I'M SURE GLAD. IT'LL GIVE US A CHANCE TO REACH THOSE TRAPPED IN THE BUILDINGS.

NICE WORK, SCOTT! LOOKS AS THOUGH WE'VE MADE IT...

YEAH! WITH THE MEDICS HERE, WE...

AN HOUR LATER, THE RING OF FIRE IS BROKEN...

SCOTT BREAKS OFF AS A DISTANT RUMBLE ECHOES IN THE AIR...

WHAT THE BLAZES WAS THAT?

S-SOUNDED LIKE ANOTHER TREMOR! COME ON...

AT POLICE HEADQUARTERS, HORRIFIED MEN LISTEN IN DISMAY...

REPORT COMING IN—EARTHQUAKE AT BIRAN!

ANOTHER AT VILAT!

A THIRD AT PORISTOL! BY THE CURSE OF IRZAN, IS THERE NO END TO THESE DISASTERS?

FOUR CITIES DESTROYED! VIRG, THERE'S SOMETHING WEIRD ABOUT ALL THIS...

FRANK BELLAMY

WHAT DO YOU MEAN?

EARTHQUAKES ARE CAUSED BY SEISMIC WAVES RADIATING AT RANDOM FROM A FOCAL POINT BENEATH THE EARTH'S CRUST...

SO...?

TASHFAR

BIRAN

VILAT

PORISTOL

WELL, LOOK! TASHFAR, BIRAN, VILAT, PORISTOL—ALL TOWNS CIRCLING THE DESERT. THE DEVASTATION HAS BEEN FOLLOWING A SET PATTERN!

WHAT ARE YOU TRYING TO SAY, BRAINS?

SIMPLY THAT THESE EARTHQUAKES MAY NOT BE THE NATURAL DISASTERS WE THOUGHT THEY WERE!

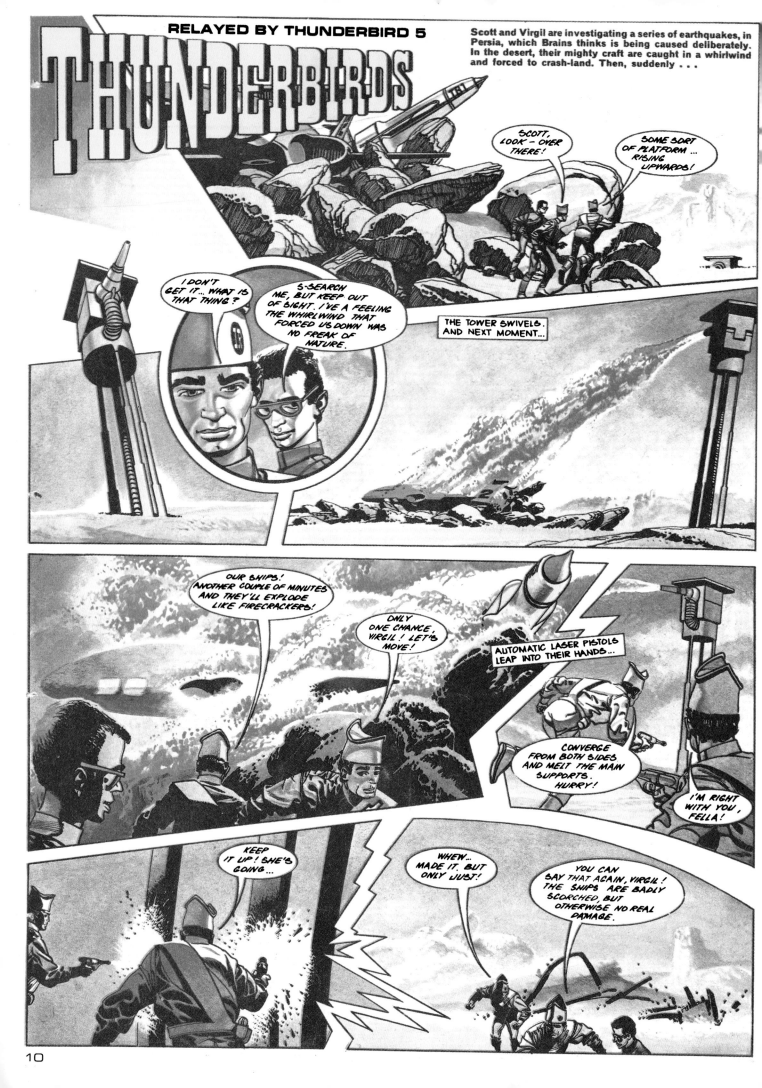

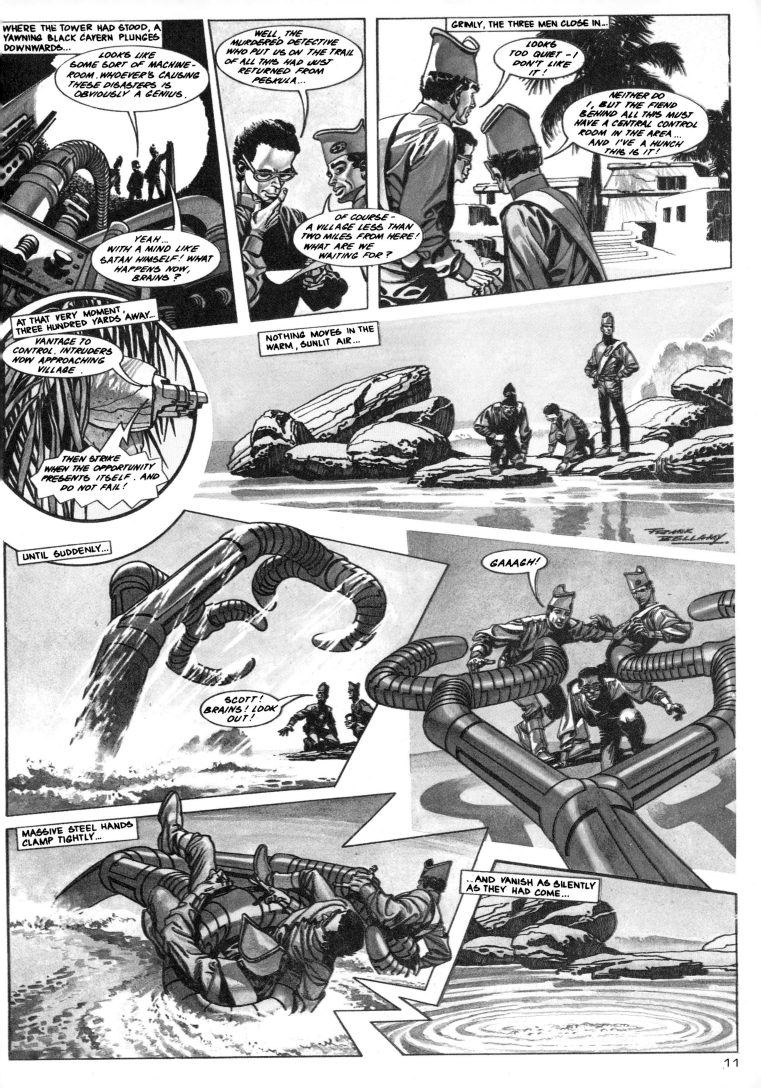

13

THUNDERBIRD 1
TECHNICAL DATA

GrahamBleathman91

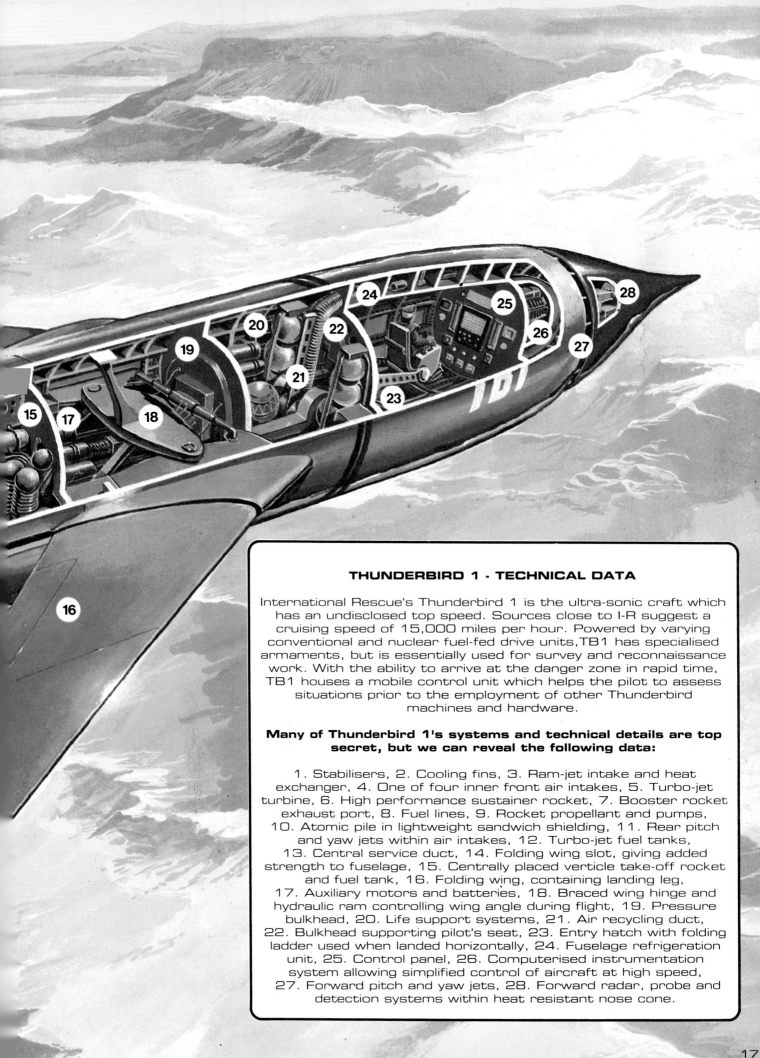

THUNDERBIRD 1 - TECHNICAL DATA

International Rescue's Thunderbird 1 is the ultra-sonic craft which has an undisclosed top speed. Sources close to I-R suggest a cruising speed of 15,000 miles per hour. Powered by varying conventional and nuclear fuel-fed drive units, TB1 has specialised armaments, but is essentially used for survey and reconnaissance work. With the ability to arrive at the danger zone in rapid time, TB1 houses a mobile control unit which helps the pilot to assess situations prior to the employment of other Thunderbird machines and hardware.

Many of Thunderbird 1's systems and technical details are top secret, but we can reveal the following data:

1. Stabilisers, 2. Cooling fins, 3. Ram-jet intake and heat exchanger, 4. One of four inner front air intakes, 5. Turbo-jet turbine, 6. High performance sustainer rocket, 7. Booster rocket exhaust port, 8. Fuel lines, 9. Rocket propellant and pumps, 10. Atomic pile in lightweight sandwich shielding, 11. Rear pitch and yaw jets within air intakes, 12. Turbo-jet fuel tanks, 13. Central service duct, 14. Folding wing slot, giving added strength to fuselage, 15. Centrally placed verticle take-off rocket and fuel tank, 16. Folding wing, containing landing leg, 17. Auxiliary motors and batteries, 18. Braced wing hinge and hydraulic ram controlling wing angle during flight, 19. Pressure bulkhead, 20. Life support systems, 21. Air recycling duct, 22. Bulkhead supporting pilot's seat, 23. Entry hatch with folding ladder used when landed horizontally, 24. Fuselage refrigeration unit, 25. Control panel, 26. Computerised instrumentation system allowing simplified control of aircraft at high speed, 27. Forward pitch and yaw jets, 28. Forward radar, probe and detection systems within heat resistant nose cone.

THUNDERBIRDS

JULY 15th, 2067... THE ATOMIC SHIP 'PRESIDENT' LEAVES NEW YORK ON ITS MAIDEN VOYAGE...

FROM TRA... IN THE PA... THUNDERB... HEADS AT... FOR NEW...

IT'S A PITY WE CAN'T GET ANY CLOSER. STILL, IF THINGS STAY THIS QUIET, WE MAY GET THE CHANCE WHEN SHE SAILS ACROSS THE PACIFIC.

LET'S TAKE A LOOK AT THE NEW CANAL, DAD. THAT'S ANOTHER PIECE OF ENGINEERING GENIUS.

F.A.B., SCOTT. THE OLD PANAMA WOULD NEVER HAVE BEEN BIG ENOUGH TO TAKE SHIPS AS LARGE AS THE PRESIDENT.

PAST TROUBLES IN THE PANAMA ZONE FORCED THE WORLD GOVERNMENT TO ORDER THE BUILDING OF A NEW CANAL ACROSS FRIENDLY NICARAGUA.

BOY, SHE'S THREE TIMES THE SIZE OF PANAMA.

YES... AND LESS TROUBLE TO CONTROL AND NAVIGATE.

IT'S AMAZING, SCOTT. NOT THIRTY MILES FROM HERE, MILLIONS OF DOLLARS HAVE BEEN SPENT ON A NEW SEAWAY, YET THOSE HOVELS HAVEN'T BEEN TOUCHED IN ONE AND A HALF CENTURIES!

PEOPLE STILL LIVE THERE, TOO, DAD...

YES... I'M AFRAID THE NICARAGUAN GOVERNMENT IS NEGLECTING THEM.

IN THE SMALL TOWN OF SAN CAGAS, JEFF'S WORDS ARE ECHOED...

WHILE THE GOVERNMENT GROWS FAT FROM THE DOLLARS PAID BY THE SHIPS ON THE CANAL, WE STARVE IN MISERY.

FRANK BELLAMY

THE LARGEST AND FASTEST LINER EVER BUILT, THE PRESIDENT IS BOUND FOR AUSTRALIA...

SURE IS GOOD TO BE OFF DUTY, DAD.

YES, SCOTT... THIS BREAK WILL GIVE US A CHANCE TO TAKE A LOOK AT THE PRESIDENT.

FLYING HIGH TO AVOID AIR CORRIDORS AND RECOGNITION, THUNDERBIRD 1 PASSES OVER THE GIANT VESSEL...

YOU'RE WITNESSING HISTORY IN THE MAKING, SCOTT.

YEAH! WHAT A MAGNIFICENT SIGHT. SHE'S FANTASTIC!

RIGHT, SON... LET'S GO HOME. WE'RE STILL IN THE RESCUE BUSINESS, REMEMBER.

I KNOW, FATHER... AND THUNDERBIRD 1 COULD BE NEEDED ON AN EMERGENCY AT ANY TIME.

THEY FLY OVER SOME OLD TOWNS AND VILLAGES...

YES... IT IS TIME WE MADE A BIG NOISE!

THE WORLD SHOULD KNOW OF OUR TROUBLES.

ONLY A SCANDAL WILL MAKE OUR GOVERNMENT LISTEN. WE MUST DO SOMETHING THAT WILL SHATTER THE WHOLE WORLD.

I HAVE IT! THE NEW SHIP, THE PRESIDENT! WE WILL BLOW HER UP!

19

THUNDERBIRDS

Embarking on its maiden voyage, the new atomic liner, *President*, sails from New York. The fantastic vessel has to pass through the newly completed canal across central America. Thrilled by these two wonders of the 21st century, Jeff Tracy orders Scott to head for home...

WE'LL TAKE ANOTHER LOOK AT THE PRESIDENT WHEN SHE REACHES THE PACIFIC.

OK, DAD, WE'VE AWAY BASE...

AND SO...

JOIN WITH US, AMIGOS. WE MUST TELL THE WORLD OF OUR POVERTY AND THE WAY OUR GOVERNMENT IS TURNING ITS BACK ON US.

BUT TO DESTROY THE BIG SHIP... THAT IS WRONG.

IS IT NOT ALSO WRONG FOR PEOPLE TO LIVE IN SQUALOR LIKE WE DO? HAVE WE NOT TRIED EVERYTHING ELSE?

YES... WE HAVE TALKED AND TALKED. NOW IT IS TIME FOR ACTION.

VILLAGE UPON VILLAGE IS VISITED...

FOLLOW US TO FREEDOM! AND LET THE EXPERTS AMONG YOU JOIN ME IN THE CANTINA.

THE EXP...

I A... GOOD ... EXPLO...

ON THE BRIDGE, CAPTAIN THOMAS CHECKS THE ROBOT SYSTEMS WITH HIS SECOND IN COMMAND.

ALL CONTROLS READ GREEN, SIR.

THANK YOU, KING. WE WILL BE AT THE CANAL HEAD BY DAYLIGHT.

JUAN DOES NOT INCLUDE BLOODSHED IN HIS PLANS.

WE WILL STOP THE PRESIDENT BY BLOCKING THE CANAL. ALL THE PASSENGERS AND CREW WILL BE ORDERED TO LEAVE.

I SEE... THEN WE WILL BLOW UP THE SHIP.

JUST A LITTLE... ENOUGH TO CAUSE AN OUTCRY.

BY NOON THAT DAY, THE PATTERN IS SET...

LOOK! SHE COMES.

DO YOU HEAR JUAN? ARE YOU READY?

WE ARE READY!

A SIGNAL IS FLASHED TO A SMALL TANKER. AT THE CONTROLS ARE CASTA AND GOLAN.

JUAN WAS CLEVER TO USE THIS VESSEL, CASTA, HE KNEW YOU WERE ITS ENGINEER.

YES... BUT HE DOES NOT KNOW OUR PLANS ARE DIFFERENT FROM HIS.

THE PRESIDENT REACH... NEAREST PART OF TH...

CAPTAIN... THAT TANKE... IT'S HEADI... STRAIGHT ... US.

WE'RE DRIFTING TOWARDS THE NORTH BANK, SIR.

HARD ASTERN... WE'LL FOUL THE BOWS!

BUT THE IMPACT OF COLLISION CANNOT BE CHECKED...

FLOODING BELOW WATER-LINE, SIR...

SEAL ALL FORWARD HOLDS... AND CHECK THIS DRIFT!

[O]N SHORE, THE MAN BEHIND [T]HE PLAN IS WORRIED...

IT IS WORSE THAN WE EXPECTED. WE HAVE CAUSED MUCH TROUBLE.

BUT NO-ONE HAS BEEN HURT. WE MUST CONTINUE OR OUR EFFORTS HAVE BEEN WASTED.

YOU ARE RIGHT, JOSE. ORDER THE PASSENGERS AND CREW TO LEAVE THE SHIP. WE MUST TELL THE WORLD OF OUR PROBLEMS.

INSTRUCTIONS ARE GIVEN, BUT UNKNOWN TO JUAN, SOME OF HIS FOLLOWERS BELIEVE IN HARSHER METHODS OF PERSUASION...

PEOPLE ABOARD THE 'PRESIDENT'. LISTEN TO ME! IF YOU SET FOOT ON OUR SOIL WE WILL SHOOT!

THUNDERBIRD 5 TO INTERNATIONAL RESCUE. COME IN, FATHER.

GO AHEAD, JOHN.

LAUNCH THUNDERBIRD 1, SCOTT. WE NEED FIRST HAND INFORMATION.

BUT FATHER... INTERNATIONAL RESCUE HAS NOT BEEN SUMMONED...

I KNOW, SCOTT. THERE ARE SOME OCCASIONS WHEN IT BECOMES NECESSARY TO INVITE OURSELVES. THIS SITUATION COULD EXPLODE AT ANY MINUTE. GET GOING!

FATHER... THERE'S BEEN A NEW DEVELOPMENT AND IT'S NOT GOOD. THE SHIP HAS DAMMED THE CANAL.

THE WATER'S RISING FAST AND IS STARTING TO FLOOD THE LOWER GROUND!

...IRD 1
...THE
...READING
...E GOT
...THING
...THAT

BUT EVENTS ARE MOVING SWIFTLY. JOHN TRACY MONITORS A DESPERATE RADIO CALL...

THIS IS THE PRESIDENT OF NICARAGUA SPEAKING. REBEL FORCES HAVE COMMITTED HOSTILE ACTS AGAINST A FRIENDLY NATION...

SCOTT TRACY IS GIVEN HIS INSTRUCTIONS...

WE'RE GOING TO DRAW UP A PLAN OF ACTION, SCOTT. STAND BY TO PASS ALL INFORMATION TO BRAINS.

F.A.B.

VERY WELL, I WILL DELAY MY FORCES FOR 24 HOURS. IF YOU HAVE NOT SUCCEEDED BY THEN, THE REBELS WILL BE PUT DOWN.

...HAVE
...NED
...RYTHING.
...CANNOT
...E FOR
...MPATHY
...OM THE
...RLD IF
...E USE
...ORCE.

...E
...UAN
...NMENT
...TAND
...ATCH...
...TO
...T
...ES.

YOU ARE WRONG, CASTA. WE MUST REMAIN PEACEFUL IF WE ARE TO WIN.

JUAN... COME QUICKLY!

THEY RUSH TO A HIGH HILL...

SEE... THE SAN PEDRO VILLAGE... IT WILL BE SWAMPED.

THIS IS OUR DOING! EVERYTHING HAS GONE WRONG!

AND MORE IS YET TO COME!

...UNDERBIRD 1
...BASE... THE
...ST VILLAGE IS
...DER WATER
...NGS ARE REAL
...AD HERE,
...FATHER.

THE TREMENDOUS WEIGHT OF WATER BURSTS THE NORTH BANK OF THE CANAL... AND A TIDAL WAVE CASCADES ACROSS THE PLATEAU!

THUNDERBIRDS

The atomic liner 'President', sabotaged by dissatisfied Nicaraguan peasants, lies across the canal. The pent-up waters have flooded the surrounding villages. Now the liner has keeled over, trapping Gordon in TB4 . . .

...EF MOMENT,
...'S
...IRD'S CREW...

BUT THEN...

RETRACT THE GRAB, VIRGIL. WE MUST GET THE SHIP CLEAR OF GORDON. SCOTT, WE'LL NEED YOU QUICKLY!

JUAN CAN STAND IDLE NO LONGER.

THE BRAVE MAN IN THE SMALL CRAFT DOWN THERE MAY BE DROWNING. WE MUST GIVE HELP.

WHAT CAN WE DO, YOU FOOL? EVEN THE GREAT MACHINES WILL NOT SAVE HIM.

BUT I CAN TRY!

MUST FIND THE DOOR... THE DOOR! I HAVE SO LITTLE TIME.

JUAN HAS DONE RIGHTLY. WE MUST ATONE FOR OUR FOOLISHNESS BY GIVING HELP.

NO! WHY SHOULD WE HELP THESE FOREIGNERS?

A WORD IN YOUR EAR, CASTA.

...G...
...RGIL!
...'S
...!

GOLON PLANS FURTHER TREACHERY...

THIS RABBLE WILL NO LONGER HEAR US. BUT I HAVE A PLAN TO TEACH THEM A LESSON—AND ALSO THESE INTERFERING FLYING-MEN. BY NOW, GOVERNMENT TROOPS MUST BE APPROACHING—AND WE WILL MEET THEM!

WE CAN'T HOLD FULL POWER MUCH LONGER, BRAINS. THE CABLES WON'T TAKE THAT STRAIN—AND NEITHER WILL THUNDERBIRD 2!

THEY MUST... FOR JUST A LITTLE LONGER.

AND JUAN IS RIGHT...

YOU MUST MAKE HASTE, GENERAL. THE REBELS HAVE BEEN JOINED BY FOREIGNERS IN HEAVILY-ARMED AIRCRAFT.

...ND
...E

THUNDERBIRDS

The sabotaged atomic liner 'President,' has blocked the Nicaraguan Canal and flooded the surrounding country. While TBs 1 and 2 try to right the liner, Juan, rebel leader of the saboteurs, rescues Gordon from TB 4 crushed beneath the liner. Juan's evil lieutenants attempt to mislead the government troops . . .

THE FOREIGNERS WILL HELP THE REBELS TO OVERTHROW THE GOVERNMENT!

COLUMN, ADVANCE! TO THE ATTACK!

BUT THE GREAT VESSEL IS STILL AGROUND...

NOW TO REPAIR THE BREACH AND REFLOAT HER. THE WATER LEVEL WILL SOON RISE AGAIN

...AND A FURTHER DANGER THREATENS.

SEE! IT MUST BE THE GOVERNMENT TROOPS.

AND I JUST HOPE THEY KNOW WE'RE ON THEIR SIDE!

THE WATERS ARE NOT DEEP FORWARD, AND FIRE AT WILL!

SCOTT ACTS...

F.A.B., VIRGIL—I'M ON MY WAY AND SO IS GORDON!

AND GORDON LEADS THE REBELS ON A FORLORN HOPE.

...MUST GET TO THE TROOPS... EXPLAIN... ONLY WAY...

IT IS CERTAIN DEATH! BUT I AM WITH YOU...

THE ADVANCE IS HALTED IN THE DENSE SMOKE-SCREEN.

I AM THE LEADER OF THE REBELS. I HAVE COME TO SURRENDER.

CALL OFF THE ATTACK, GENERAL, AND LISTEN TO ME...

THE SMOKE BEGINS TO CLEAR.

...JUAN AND HIS PEOPLE HAD A TRUE GRIEVANCE—BUT NEVER PLANNED TO ENDANGER LIFE. THEY WERE BETRAYED...

SOLDIERS—THOSE TWO ARE TO BE KEPT UNDER HEAVY GUARD. WE KNOW HOW TO DEAL WITH TRAITORS!

THE BREACH IN THE CANAL WALL HAS BEEN ALMOST FILLED.

THUNDERBIRD 2
TECHNICAL DATA

Fantastic in its power and strength, Thunderbird 2 is
constructed of an alloy developed by Hiram Heckenbacker,
fondly known to the International Rescue team as "Brains".
With interchangeable Pods, Thunderbird 2 carries vital heavy
engineering and life saving equipment at speed to the danger zone.
An estimated cruising speed of 2000 m.p.h. has been recorded
and optimum altitude for TB2 is 60,000 feet, but as with other
International Rescue craft and systems, much of the technical data
is secret. We are however, able to reveal the following details:

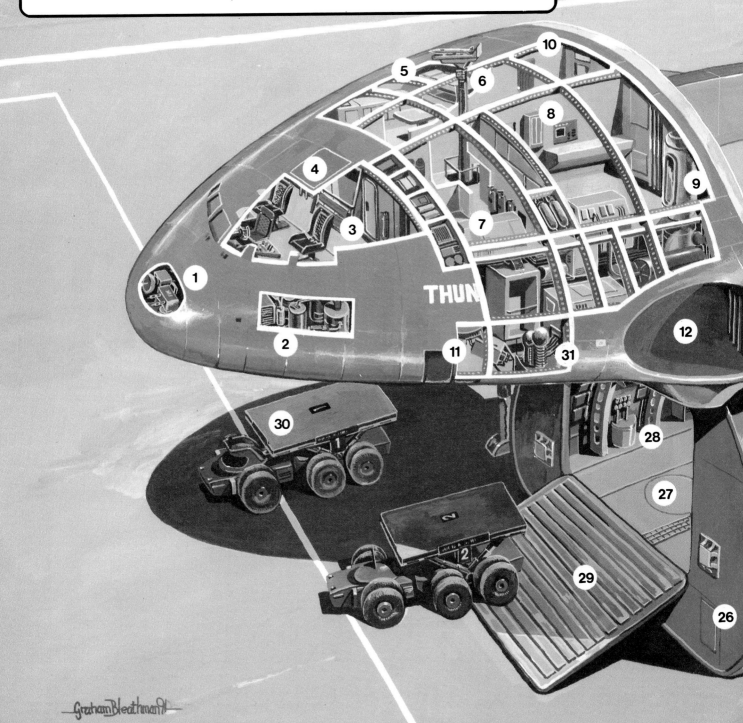

Graham Bleathman 91

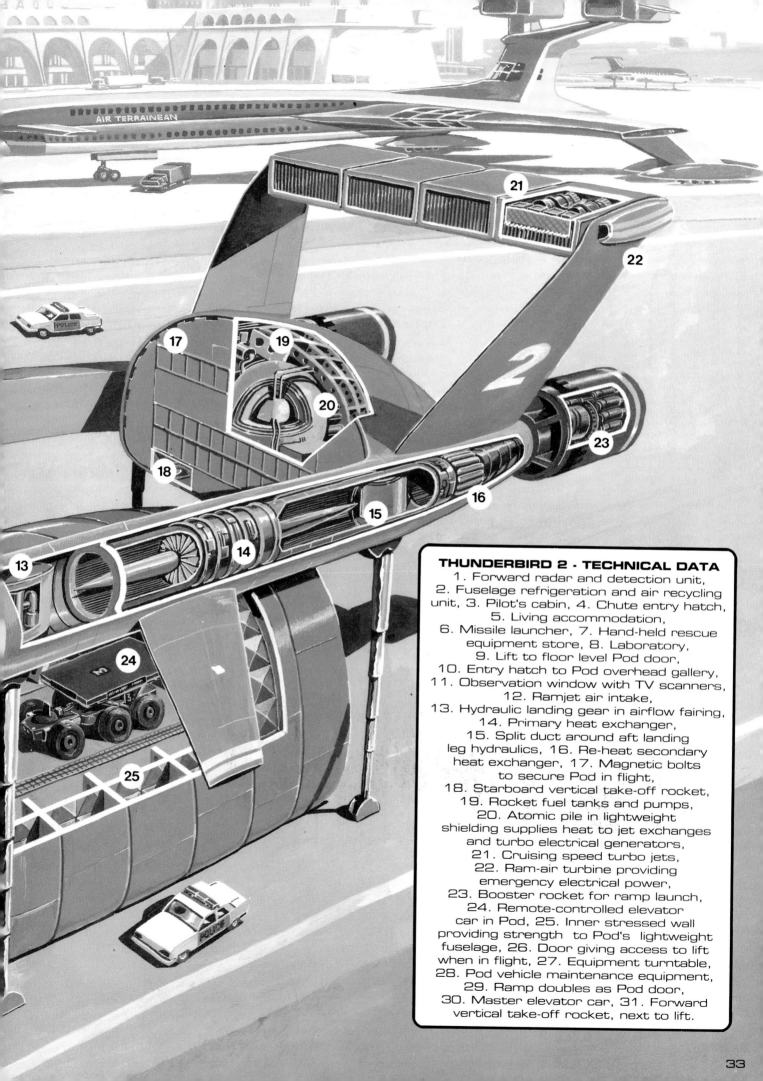

THUNDERBIRD 2 · TECHNICAL DATA

1. Forward radar and detection unit,
2. Fuselage refrigeration and air recycling unit, 3. Pilot's cabin, 4. Chute entry hatch,
5. Living accommodation,
6. Missile launcher, 7. Hand-held rescue equipment store, 8. Laboratory,
9. Lift to floor level Pod door,
10. Entry hatch to Pod overhead gallery,
11. Observation window with TV scanners,
12. Ramjet air intake,
13. Hydraulic landing gear in airflow fairing,
14. Primary heat exchanger,
15. Split duct around aft landing leg hydraulics, 16. Re-heat secondary heat exchanger, 17. Magnetic bolts to secure Pod in flight,
18. Starboard vertical take-off rocket,
19. Rocket fuel tanks and pumps,
20. Atomic pile in lightweight shielding supplies heat to jet exchanges and turbo electrical generators,
21. Cruising speed turbo jets,
22. Ram-air turbine providing emergency electrical power,
23. Booster rocket for ramp launch,
24. Remote-controlled elevator car in Pod, 25. Inner stressed wall providing strength to Pod's lightweight fuselage, 26. Door giving access to lift when in flight, 27. Equipment turntable,
28. Pod vehicle maintenance equipment,
29. Ramp doubles as Pod door,
30. Master elevator car, 31. Forward vertical take-off rocket, next to lift.

THUNDERBIRDS

The search for more efficient methods is continual at the island base of International Rescue. Thunderbird machines must be equipped with instruments that can overcome the most arduous weather conditions experienced by man . . .

IN THE COMMAND SECTOR BUILDING, A TOP LEVEL CONFERENCE IS IN PROGRESS.

CONDITIONS WILL BE AT THEIR WORST TOMORROW AFTERNOON. I RECOMMEND THE GREEN LIGHT.

AGREED, LASER MISSILE DESTRUCTOR WILL OPERATE AT FOURTEEN HUNDRED HOURS —WEDNESDAY.

CAMP 21st CENTURY WORLD ARMY BASE

COMMAND SECTOR

GENTLEMEN, IF THESE TESTS ARE SUCCESSFUL WE WILL HAVE ACHIEVED A MAJOR BREAKTHROUGH IN THE EXTREME WEATHER DEFENCE PROGRAMME.

YES, SIR. I'LL ISSUE THE BLANKET CLEARANCE ORDER.

INTERNATION... ORBITING S... PICKS UP TH... MESSAGE...

WITH A FINAL WARNING TO STAY CLEAR OF CAMP 21st CENTURY, SCOTT LIFTS OFF...

FOURTEEN HUNDRED HOURS APPROACHES AT CAMP 21st CENTURY...

21st CENTURY TO TARGET MOTHER GREENLAND. IGNITE MISSILE... COURSE SEVEN-FOUR-THREE POLAR!

ROGER 21st CENTURY.

GREENLAND IS A WORLD NAVY MISSILE CARRIER.

FRANK BELLAMY

DESPITE THE AWFUL CONDITIONS THE LASERS HAVE FOUND AND DESTROYED THE TARGET...

ONE RAY FINDS THE MISSILE AND HOLDS THE TARGET... NEXT SECOND THE OTHER RAY MAKES CONTACT AND...

EMERGENCY RED! MISSILE OUT OF CONTROL. CRASH COURSE— REACTOR BUILDING.

...BEHIND RESEARCH
...ENT IS BRAINS...

...ONS RIGHT
...CTIC TESTS,
...S?

YES,
MR. TRACY.
THE WEATHER
IS IDEAL.

ON TOP OF THE WORLD A BLIZZARD
IS RAGING OVER THE WORLD ARMY
BASE KNOWN AS CAMP 21st CENTURY
WHICH IS FIFTY FEET BENEATH
THE ICE CAP...

NOW
HEAR THIS!
MAXIMUM SECURITY
ORDER. IMPERATIVE
POLAR REGIONS
7, 8 AND 9 ARE
AVOIDED!

JOHN TRACY RELAYS THE
INFORMATION TO TRACY
ISLAND...

THUNDERBIRD 5 TO BASE.
CAMP 21st CENTURY HAS PUT
UP THE FLIGHT BAN TO ALL
AIRLINES AND COMMUNICATIONS,
FATHER.

THANKS,
SON... WE'LL BE
WELL CLEAR OF
THAT AREA SO OUR
POLAR TESTS CAN
CONTINUE AS
PLANNED.

EIGHTEEN HOURS PASS...

OKAY, SCOTT...
YOU'RE FAMILIAR
WITH THE NEW
ARCTIC AND SUB
ZERO SYSTEMS IN
THUNDERBIRD 1.

YES,
FATHER. IF
BRAINS IS RIGHT,
I'LL HAVE NO
TROUBLE WITH
THE POLAR
WEATHER.

THE MISSILE FLIES INTO
THE TREACHEROUS
WEATHER GUIDED ON
A FIXED PATH...

THEN, ACTIVATED FROM
BENEATH THE ICE, TWIN
LASER RAYS SEEK OUT
THE MISSILE...

CAUTION
...ADIATION AREA

THUNDERBIRDS

There has been a disaster at Camp 21st Century, a World Army Arctic base under the ice cap. A wayward missile has crashed and destroyed the nuclear power plant . . .

A SH...
DOWN
BLAST

INSTANTLY, CAMP 21st CENTURY IS PLUNGED INTO COLD DARKNESS...

THE STANDBY GENERATOR IS ACTIVATED...

HOW LONG WILL IT LAST, SERGEANT?

TWO WEEKS, LIEUTENANT... BUT THE BATTERIES MUST BE KEPT TO MAXIMUM CHARGE LEVEL.

SWITCH TO EMERGENCY POWER PLANT... HURRY... WE'LL ALL FREEZE TO DEATH.

AN IMM
HELD B

TH
IS T
SITUA
THE FI
THE RE
CHAMB
STILL
BLAZIN

ON TRACY ISLAND, JEFF LISTENS TO HIS SON...

THEIR ONLY HOPE IS BY SEA.

RIGHT, JOHN... LINK ME WITH THUNDERBIRD 1...

MILES FROM CAMP 21st CENTURY, THUNDERBIRD 1 IS UNDERGOING SUB ZERO INSTRUMENT CHECKS...

BASE TO THUNDERBIRD 1... HOW'S IT GOING, SCOTT?

AT CAPE ADAIR, BAFFIN ISLAND, CAPTAIN TERENCE BATON RECEIVES HIS ORDERS...

RIGHT, CAPTAIN. YOU KNOW THE URGENCY OF THIS MISSION. GET THAT REACTOR TO CAMP 21st CENTURY WITHOUT FAIL!

YES, SIR... LEAVE IT TO ME.

ICE BREAKER SHACKLETON STARTS ON ITS FIVE HUNDRED MILE JOURNEY NORTHWARDS...

PRO
GOOD

...VE TRAVELS LIKE A E JET...

... HITS THE REACTOR... AND EXPLODES!

CONFERENCE IS ASE COMMANDERS...

YES, GENERAL... BUT WE'VE MANAGED TO CONFINE IT TO THE ANTI-RADIATION SHIELDS.

THE FLAMES WON'T GET THROUGH THOSE LEAD WALLS IN A HURRY... LET'S HOPE THE BLAZE BURNS ITSELF OUT.

OUR IMMEDIATE WORRY IS TO GET A NEW REACTOR UP HERE... AND THAT LITTLE BOX OF TRICKS WILL HAVE TO COME FROM BAFFIN ISLAND.

THE URGENT RADIO CALLS FROM THE TOP OF THE WORLD ARE MONITORED BY JOHN TRACY IN THUNDERBIRD 5...

I THINK THEY'LL HAVE TROUBLE, FATHER. THE CONDITIONS RULE OUT ANY HELP FROM CONVENTIONAL AIRCRAFT.

YOU MIGHT HAVE TO! I WANT YOU TO CHECK OUT BAFFIN BAY SEA CONDITIONS.

THUNDERBIRD 1 TURNS TO HEAD AWAY FROM THE BITTER ARCTIC WEATHER...

GREAT, ...HER. WITH ...W EQUIPMENT ...D SET THUNDERBIRD 1 ... ON A DOLLAR NOTE ...CED AT THE NORTH POLE!

INSTRUMENTS RECORD UNUSUALLY SEVERE ICE CONDITIONS AHEAD, SIR.

...N'T BE ... LIEUTENANT... ... HAVE TO TAKE ...HANCES. THE ...KLETON IS ... BREAKER, ...U KNOW!

THE CHANCES ARE NOT GOOD.

WE'RE LOSING SPEED!

YES, SIR... I'M AFRAID WE'RE NOT GOING TO MAKE IT!

FRANK BELLAMY

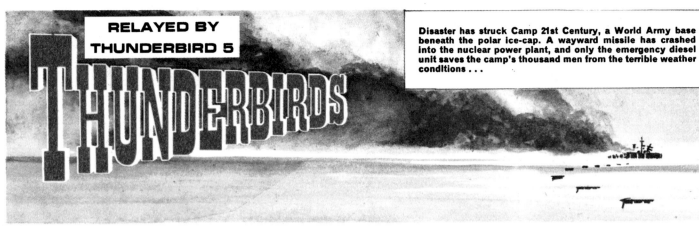

RELAYED BY THUNDERBIRD 5

THUNDERBIRDS

Disaster has struck Camp 21st Century, a World Army base beneath the polar ice-cap. A wayward missile has crashed into the nuclear power plant, and only the emergency diesel unit saves the camp's thousand men from the terrible weather conditions . . .

AS THE SHIP STRIKES FURTHER NORTHWARDS, PROGRESS DIMINISHES...

THE ENGINES ARE AT FULL POWER, SIR...

IT'S NOT FAST ENOUGH! WE'LL NEVER MAKE IT IN TIME.

IN ANOTHER REGION OF THE POLAR WASTES, THUNDERBIRD 1 HAS BEEN ON ARCTIC TRIALS.

IT'S REALLY BAD UP HERE, FATHER. THANK GOODNESS I'VE GOT THE NEW POLAR NAVIGATION EQUIPMENT ABOARD.

SUDDENLY...

THE SCIENTISTS RUSH TO THE COMMAND SECTOR AND WITHIN MINUTES A WARNING ECHOES THROUGH THE ICE TUNNELS...

EMERGENCY—PRIORITY ONE! REACTOR CHAMBER HAS FRACTURED... RADIATION RISK: ALARM RED!

THIS IS DEADLY SERIOUS, GENTLEMEN... NO ONE CAN LEAVE THE PROTECTION OF THESE BUILDINGS.

THE FANS BREAK UP THE CINDER... BUT SPARKS REACH THE DIESEL GENERATOR FUEL STORES...

A CINDER CAREERS OVER THE ICE... AND IS DRAWN INTO AN AIR INTAKE SHAFT...

...HE NUCLEAR REACTOR CHAMBER IS AN INFERNO. ANTI-RADIATION SHIELDS SEAL AND CONTAIN THE FIRE...

THERE IS ONLY SEVEN DAY'S FUEL LEFT AND ICE-BREAKER SHACKLETON HAS THAT AMOUNT OF TIME TO DELIVER A NEW REACTOR...

FRANK BELLAMY

HOW DOES IT LOOK FOR THE SHACKLETON, SCOTT?

HOPELESS, FATHER... SHE'LL NEVER GET THROUGH THAT ICE.

VIRGIL IS STANDING BY, THUNDERBIRD 2 MAY BE NEEDED TO FERRY FUEL TO THE ARCTIC. THOSE MEN WILL DIE IF THAT GENERATOR FAILS...

AT CAMP 21ST. CENTURY, ARMY SCIENTISTS KEEP CONSTANT WATCH ON THE REACTOR CHAMBER SHIELDS...

REACTOR CHAMBER

PHEW... THAT FIRE WILL LAST FOR MONTHS.

YES! SAY, FRANK... THIS PART OF THE SHIELD IS WEAKENING. LOOK AT THE READING I'M PICKING UP!

...ERAL, ...DON'T... ...TOO ...!...

THE SCIENTIST COLLAPSES...

GENERAL... THIS MAN HAS RADIATION SICKNESS! HE MUST HAVE BEEN CONTAMINATED WHEN THAT SHIELD CRACKED!

OUTSIDE, THE RAGING BLIZZARD CONTINUES, WHIPPING AWAY THE EDDIES OF SPARKS THAT LEAP FROM THE REACTOR WASTE SHAFTS...

ALL POWER IS AT AN END. A FRANTIC RADIO SIGNAL FROM CAMP 21ST CENTURY REACHES THUNDERBIRD 5...

THUNDERBIRD 5

5

ONE THOUSAND MEN ARE HELPLESS... THEY'RE TRAPPED BELOW THE ICE AND WILL EITHER FREEZE OR BE CONTAMINATED!

THERE DOESN'T SEEM TO BE ANY HOPE! THEY'RE ALL DOOMED TO A TERRIBLE DEATH!

THUNDERBIRDS

RELAYED BY THUNDERBIRD 5

In Camp 21st Century, fifty feet below the Arctic Ice Cap, one thousand men face death. A reactor has exploded leaving the base without power, and radiation is polluting the tunnels. A raging blizzard rules out any possibility of conventional rescue attempts...

SCOTT WILL GUIDE YOU THROUGH THE BLIZZARD, VIRGIL!

YES. AS SOON AS YOU ARRIVE, ALAN WILL TAKE CARE OF THE REACTOR FIRE IN FIREFLY WHILST YOU HOOK UP TO THE BASE AND SUPPLY POWER!

OF COURSE! THUNDERBIRD 2'S ENGINES COULD KEEP THE PLACE GOING FOR A COUPLE OF DAYS!

SURE. LET'S GET MOVING, FELLERS'!

THUNDERBIRD 2 MAKES READY FOR TAKE OFF...

OKAY, ALAN... GET READY TO FIRE THE LOW YIELD MISSILE!

F.A.B.!

NEXT SECOND...

THE MISSILE PENETRATES THE THICK ICE AND EXPLODES...

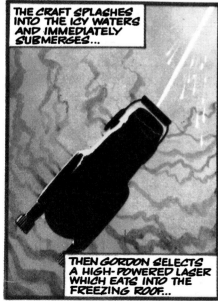

THE CRAFT SPLASHES INTO THE ICY WATERS AND IMMEDIATELY SUBMERGES...

THEN GORDON SELECTS A HIGH-POWERED LASER WHICH EATS INTO THE FREEZING ROOF...

THUNDERBIRD 1, FITTED WITH SPECIAL POLAR REGION NAVIGATION EQUIPMENT, MEETS THUNDERBIRD 2...

THUNDERBIRD 2 FROM THUNDERBIRD 1 COCKPIT... STAY CLOSE, VIRGIL. YOUR CONTROL SYSTEMS WILL NEVER GET YOU THROUGH THIS BLIZZARD IF YOU LOSE ME!

INTERNATIONAL RESCUE PREPARES FOR ACTION...

THERE'S NOT MUCH HOPE FOR THOSE MEN, BUT BRAINS HAS WORKED OUT A PLAN. WE MUST AT LEAST TRY TO SAVE THEM!

FIRST WE MUST FREE THAT SHIP SO THAT IT CAN GET THE REPLACEMENT REACTOR TO THE CAMP. THUNDERBIRD 2 WILL TAKE THUNDERBIRD 4 TO THE SPOT AND THEN GO ON TO THE BASE...

FRANK BELLAMY

...AND IS SOON SPEEDING TOWARDS THE POLAR REGIONS

TRAPPED IN THE ICE OF BAFFIN BAY, THE 'SHACKLETON' LIES HELPLESS...

A HOLE HAS BEEN MADE... LARGE ENOUGH FOR THUNDERBIRD 4 TO ENTER...

HEY, VIRGIL... FLY BELOW ME AND SEE IF YOU CAN SPOT THE TROUBLE!

SCOTT... YOU'RE ICING UP! THUNDERBIRD 1'S FUSELAGE HEATING SYSTEMS ARE INACTIVE!

WHAT CAN WE DO, VIRGIL? SCOTT WILL CRASH!

PROGRESS IN CLOSE ON, THUNDERBIRD 1 SLIGHTLY...

THUNDERBIRDS

Fifty feet below the Arctic ice cap, the men in Camp 21st Century face death by freezing or radiation contamination. Thunderbird 1 leads Thunderbird 2 through a raging blizzard. Then Thunderbird 1's heating systems cease . . .

GAUGING DISTANCE AND SPEED VIRGIL FIRES HIS DOWN-THRUST ROCKETS...

OKAY, VIRGIL.... AS SOON AS WE ARE DOWN WE'LL GET MY HEATING SYSTEMS FIXED AND I'LL RUSH THAT INJURED MAN TO HOSPITAL!

THE PLAN WORKS. THUNDERBIRD 1 IS ABLE TO CONTINUE AND GUIDES THUNDERBIRD 2 TO CAMP 21ST CENTURY...

BETTER PUT ON OUR ANTI-RADIATION SUITS... THE PERSONNEL DOWN THERE ARE CONFINED TO THEIR QUARTERS!

PROTEC
THE DEA
ACTIVITY
AND VIR
MAN AB
THUNDE

CAMP 21ST CENTURY

AHEAD ALL ENGINES! FULL POWER!

THUNDERBIRD 4 STAYS AHEAD OF THE 'SHACKLETON', CARVING A PATH THROUGH THE ICE...

MEANWHILE, THUNDERBIRD 1 IS MAKING GOOD PROGRESS...

THUNDERBIRD 1 TO THUNDERBIRD 2. HOW'S IT GOING, VIRGIL?

ALL
THE
OUT A
RADI
IS A

FIREFLY TO THUNDERBIRD 2. ABOUT TO ENTER REACTOR TUNNEL. HEAT AND RADIATION SHIELDS IN PLACE!

DEEPER AND DEEPER INTO THE TUNNEL SYSTEMS GOES THE FIREFLY UNTIL IT REACHES THE INFERNO CAUSED BY THE EXPLODING REACTOR...

PR
SLOW
IS A

NITRO-GLYCERINE SHELLS BLAST INTO THE HEART OF THE BLAZE AS ALAN TRIES TO EFFECT A 'BLOW-OUT'!..

FRANK BELLAMY

ERE'S ONLY ONE I'LL HAVE TO TRY T THE ICE WITH RBIRD 2!

SURE, VIRG... IF THUNDERBIRD 1 IS FORCED DOWN WE'LL NEVER MAKE IT TO THOSE MEN ON OUR OWN!

THUNDERBIRD 2 CHANGES POSITION...

AINST P10— ALAN THE ...

RIGHT, ALAN... LET'S GET THUNDERBIRD 2 CONNECTED UP... WE'VE GOT TO GET POWER DOWN INTO THOSE BUILDINGS!

YEAH... AND WE MUST DE-CONTAMINATE THE CORRIDORS!

MEANWHILE, GORDON TRACY IS IN THUNDERBIRD 4 BENEATH THE ICE PACKS OF BAFFIN BAY.

A HIGH-POWERED LASER MELTS THE FROZEN WATER...

THE ICE BREAKER 'SHACKLETON HAS A REPLACEMENT ATOMIC REACTOR ABOARD...

CAPTAIN... LOOK! THE ICE IS MELTING!

YOU'RE RIGHT, NUMBER ONE. THAT GUY DOWN THERE IS DOING A GREAT JOB!

THE POD ENTRANCE LOWERS...

SCOTT. THAWING E ELIMINATED AZARD. ALAN D TAKE CARE FIRE!

THE FIREFLY IS THE WORLD'S MOST EFFECTIVE FIRE-FIGHTING MACHINE...

SUDDENLY...

AAGH!

FIREFLY IS SLAMMED BACKWARDS BY THE POWERFUL BLAST...

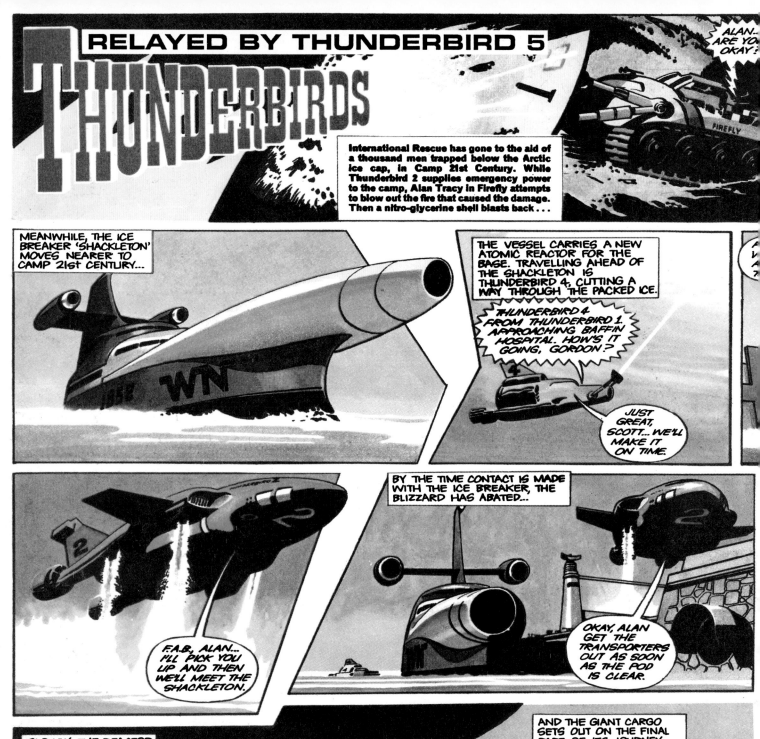

45

LAUNCH SEQUENCE:
THUNDERBIRD 1

When a call for help is received, the reconnaissance craft Thunderbird 1 is the first to be launched. Pilot Scott Tracy grips light brackets in the lounge (panel 1), triggering a revolving door and floor which spins him into TB1's hangar under the house. The wall turns back into place as Scott steps forward on to the gantry (panel 2), which feeds forward to the entry hatch in TB1 (panel 3).

Having quickly changed into uniform, Scott sits at the controls of TB1 carrying out pre-flight checks as the craft is carried down to the Launch Bay on a computer-controlled trolley.

TB1 emerges from the tunnel to the Launch Bay located under the swimming pool in front of the house. The trolley comes to a halt over the Exhaust Blast Pit, and a brief automated countdown begins.

The swimming pool, concealing the entrance to the Launch Bay, slides back under the patio.

Thunderbird 1 blasts off. When returning to base, the launch procedure is reversed, with re-entry under the control of a computer guidance system.

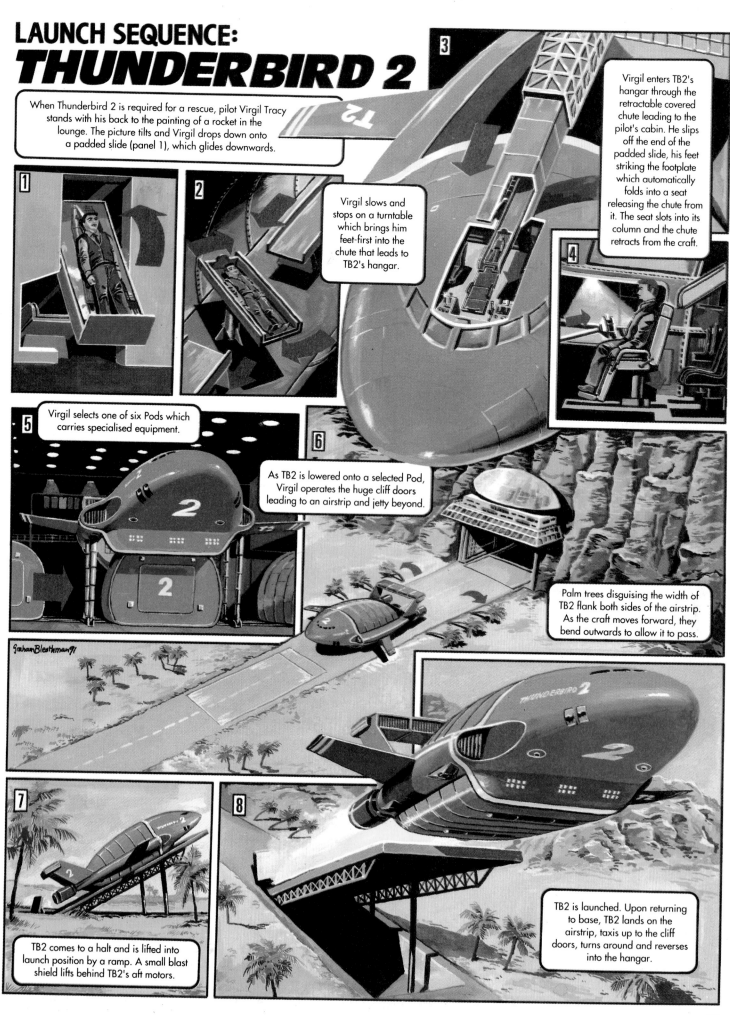

LAUNCH SEQUENCE:
THUNDERBIRD 2

When Thunderbird 2 is required for a rescue, pilot Virgil Tracy stands with his back to the painting of a rocket in the lounge. The picture tilts and Virgil drops down onto a padded slide (panel 1), which glides downwards.

3 Virgil enters TB2's hangar through the retractable covered chute leading to the pilot's cabin. He slips off the end of the padded slide, his feet striking the footplate which automatically folds into a seat releasing the chute from it. The seat slots into its column and the chute retracts from the craft.

2 Virgil slows and stops on a turntable which brings him feet-first into the chute that leads to TB2's hangar.

5 Virgil selects one of six Pods which carries specialised equipment.

6 As TB2 is lowered onto a selected Pod, Virgil operates the huge cliff doors leading to an airstrip and jetty beyond.

Palm trees disguising the width of TB2 flank both sides of the airstrip. As the craft moves forward, they bend outwards to allow it to pass.

GrahamBleathman 91

7 TB2 comes to a halt and is lifted into launch position by a ramp. A small blast shield lifts behind TB2's aft motors.

8 TB2 is launched. Upon returning to base, TB2 lands on the airstrip, taxis up to the cliff doors, turns around and reverses into the hangar.